TRANS FORMERS

DARK OF THE MOON

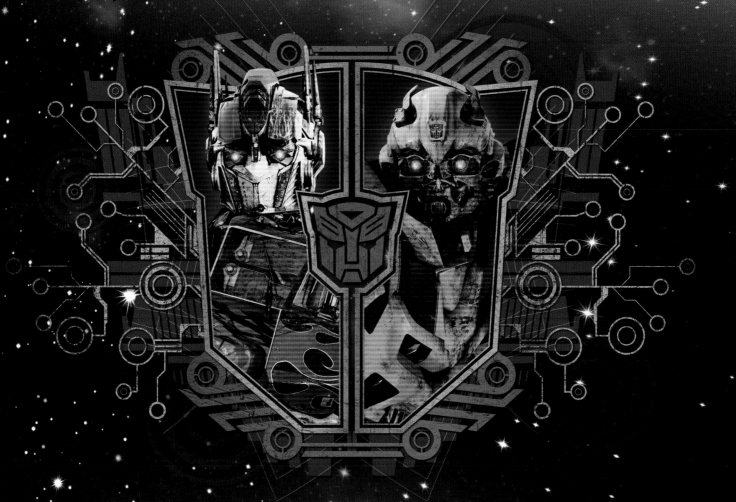

ANNUAL 2012

HarperCollins *Children's Books*

Licensed By:

GM

TRANSFORMERS © 2011 Hasbro. All Rights Reserved.
© 2011 Paramount Pictures Corporation. All Rights Reserved.
978-0-00-743624-8
1 3 5 7 9 10 8 6 4 2
First published in the UK by HarperCollins Children's Books in 2011

www.harpercollins.co.uk
Printed and bound in China

Written by Paddy Kempshall

CONTENTS

THE FLIGHT OF THE ARK

A long time ago, Cybertron

From the shattered wreck of a building, Optimus Prime watched as fires raged across the surface of his home planet. The long civil war on Cybertron between the Autobots and Decepticons looked to be coming to an end – and it was not a good end for the Autobots.

The Autobots had fought long and hard for their planet, but the Decepticon attack had been too powerful. Their assaults had been fierce and without mercy, leaving the Autobot army split into tiny groups. These small squads of Autobots were no match for the number of Decepticons who attacked without end.

The planet was in ruins. Fires burned wherever Optimus looked, and the sky was criss-crossed with smoke and the engine trails of Decepticon fighters. Things looked bad...

But all was not lost. As Optimus raised his eyes to the grey sky he caught sight of the huge Autobot spaceship, the Ark. Its engines flared brightly as it slowly rose into the sky and built up speed, ready to blast into space and escape.

If the Ark can escape from Cybertron, there might still be hope, Optimus thought to himself. For a moment, it looked as if Optimus might get his wish.

But suddenly, Decepticon fighters streaked into view. Much faster than the Ark, they soon caught up and raced in front of it, forcing it away from the safety of the sky and back towards the surface of the planet. With a deafening shriek, they curved back and their ion cannons sprang to life as they blasted away at the escaping ship.

Twisting and turning, the Ark dodged and weaved through the ruined buildings. With amazing skill, the pilot swooped and rolled through the ion blasts, making himself a hard target for the Decepticon fighters. Optimus watched in amazement and hope as the Decepticon fighters tried again and again to blast the ship to pieces. But they just couldn't seem to hit it.

9

The Decepticon fighters were fast, but the Autobot pilot was so good that, little by little, the Ark pulled away and started to build up a lead. Eventually it looked as if it was out of range of the fighters' cannons. With a massive blast from its engines, the Ark pointed its nose to the heavens and surged upwards towards space, and freedom.

Just as Optimus was feeling hopeful that the ship may escape and breathe new life into the Autobot fight, another Decepticon fighter swooped into view. This time the pilot of the Ark was not so lucky...

With deadly accuracy and speed, the Decepticon fighter opened fire. The blasts from its ion cannons scored a direct hit, scorching an enormous hole across the side of the Ark. Metal melted and twisted as the Autobot ship shuddered, leaking fuel and smoke into the skies. Suddenly, there was an enormous explosion and a huge ball of fire spurted out of the ship, blowing off its cargo doors and sending it spinning out of control.

"No!" cried Optimus in horror.

He watched, helpless, as the damaged ship continued to spin off course, heading for space in a trail of flames.

Their plan had failed.

Optimus Prime lowered his head to the battlefield below. He realised that there would be no quick or easy end to the war. Worse than that, he feared there was no longer any hope of an Autobot victory.

But they were Autobots, and Autobots never give up. *The Decepticons may have won this battle*, thought Optimus. *But the war will continue, and in some other place and time, there may still be hope...*

CONTINUED ON PAGE 16.

11

DATA DELIVERY

NEST has received this muddled message. Can you help by finding all these names in the jumble of data below? The words may be horizontal, vertical, diagonal or even backwards.

MEGATRON   **SHOCKWAVE**   **CYBERTRON**   **MUDFLAP**
OPTIMUS PRIME   **SENTINEL PRIME**   **MOON**   **IRONHIDE**
SAM   **ARK**   **SKIDS**   **SIDESWIPE**

Z	S	U	S	O	P	T	I	M	U	S	P	R	I	M	E	Y	I	K	U
S	J	K	Q	H	L	M	T	V	E	L	W	P	D	X	H	P	H	N	G
C	W	U	I	X	M	U	D	F	L	A	P	P	C	O	W	O	B	P	J
Y	L	Z	F	D	P	D	V	E	L	N	L	N	F	N	P	D	J	J	Z
O	O	A	Q	M	S	S	B	A	G	C	Q	Q	B	B	W	P	R	Z	E
L	V	R	K	U	Q	Y	A	U	N	D	D	X	D	S	M	T	E	V	Q
M	F	K	E	M	I	R	P	L	E	N	I	T	N	E	S	T	A	I	G
J	J	I	F	Z	D	F	K	U	Q	F	B	O	Z	V	C	W	J	Z	Z
M	R	L	F	W	B	S	C	S	L	K	Y	M	M	G	K	A	N	T	G
G	N	A	W	J	C	M	K	O	Y	N	X	X	M	C	K	P	A	Y	P
L	Z	I	N	S	T	E	Y	R	O	S	X	P	O	M	D	V	S	Q	N
E	R	Z	H	C	O	G	F	P	M	D	C	H	W	S	R	M	D	B	O
E	R	U	N	P	L	A	C	I	J	R	S	V	M	M	L	R	D	L	R
D	F	A	E	V	M	T	H	X	J	A	Y	W	D	A	Q	V	U	E	T
I	F	G	T	O	X	R	O	B	K	A	T	N	M	S	T	M	W	P	R
H	E	N	J	E	L	O	F	M	L	V	D	G	T	P	L	H	J	A	E
N	Y	C	P	Y	V	N	R	K	N	X	X	K	M	M	W	P	Z	G	B
O	L	L	C	X	H	G	D	H	V	P	O	E	Q	T	O	C	S	J	Y
R	N	S	I	D	E	S	W	I	P	E	W	M	U	I	Y	O	W	F	C
I	D	J	M	Y	Y	B	D	O	V	G	G	F	H	U	S	U	N	V	C

BITS AND BYTES

This computer file of Shockwave has corrupted. Can you recover the file by finding the shapes which exactly match the missing pieces?

13

THE BATTLE FOR CYBERTRON

HOW TO PLAY:

1. Decide who will be Optimus Prime and who will be Megatron.
2. Cut out the counters and divide them between the players.
3. Flip a coin to see who goes first.
4. Each player takes it in turn to place one of their counters in a space on the board.
5. The first player to get three of their counters in a line (either horizontally, vertically or diagonally) is the winner. If no one gets three counters in a row, play again – but the other player gets to go first this time. If you don't want to cut your Annual, use five coins or plastic counters each instead.

CHOOSE YOUR SIDE AND BATTLE YOUR OPPONENT FOR CONTROL OF CYBERTRON!

15

THE DARK SIDE OF THE MOON

CONTINUED FROM PAGE 11.

July 20, 1969, Earth and the moon

Surrounded by TV monitors and computers, the whole of Mission Control at NASA waited nervously. They watched in silence as the grey surface of the moon drifted past on a blurry black and white screen.

This was a huge moment – if the Apollo 11 craft landed safely, it would be the first time that man had ever set foot on the moon, and no one had any idea what they would find there. No one except the handful of mysterious men also watching from a second, secret control room nearby, that is...

"Sixty seconds," came a voice over the speakers.

Suddenly, everyone was very worried – the landing craft only had sixty seconds of fuel left, and it still hadn't landed. This could be a disaster. If it ran out of fuel before touching down, the landing craft would surely crash...

All eyes were glued to the TV screens and it seemed as if the whole world was holding its breath.

"Thirty seconds..."

The image on screen went black and the whole of Mission Control fell silent. Suddenly a crackly voice came out of the speakers.

"Houston, Tranquility Base here. The Eagle has landed."

The landing craft was safely down.

Just as everyone was congratulating each other, the transmission from the moon suddenly went dead. The room erupted into action, with people checking monitors and connections.

"Seems to be a transmitter malfunction," one of the technicians called.

But little did they know, someone had actually cut the communications on purpose. Inside the secret second control room, one of the mysterious men stepped forward out of the shadows and spoke into the microphone.

"Neil, you are dark on the rock. Mission is a go. You have twenty one minutes..."

At that command, the two astronauts on the moon, Neil Armstrong and Buzz Aldrin, set about their real mission – to locate a UFO they had detected crashing there nearly eight years ago!

Bouncing across the grey, powdery surface, the two astronauts headed up the edge of a crater. As they reached the top, they couldn't believe their eyes – buried in the surface was a huge alien spacecraft.

Making their way towards it, the astronauts reported back to the secret control room:

"The hull has been breached – extensive damage," said Aldrin.

Passing through the massive hole in the side of the ship, the two men carefully entered the shadows and stepped inside the gloomy ship.

"No signs of life or movement, Control," Armstrong said, as he shone his torch over the burned-out machinery inside.

The two men ventured deeper inside until they came across an enormous room. Stretching far off above their heads, the room was packed full of alien machinery, and everything was covered in a thick layer of grey dust. It had to be the ship's main control room.

The shadows seemed to stretch on for ever, and the room was eerily dark and still. As Armstrong swung his torch around, he suddenly froze in his tracks – there in front of him was a giant metal robot, silent and still in the dust on the floor.

"Houston, you cannot believe what we're seeing," Armstrong reported.

"We've got extra-terrestrials."

"Roger that. Take photos and samples and get them home safe," replied the mysterious man in the control room. "I guess we're not alone after all."

"No, Sir," replied Aldrin in disbelief. "We are not alone..."

But this was an even more important discovery than anyone realised. What the two astronauts had found was the crashed wreck of the Ark, and the lifeless body of the original Autobot leader, Sentinel Prime...

CONTINUED ON PAGE 26.

MOON MAZE

Help the Autobots find their way across the dark side of the moon to reach the Ark and rescue Sentinel Prime. Make sure you don't get stuck in any craters on the way!

START

FINISH

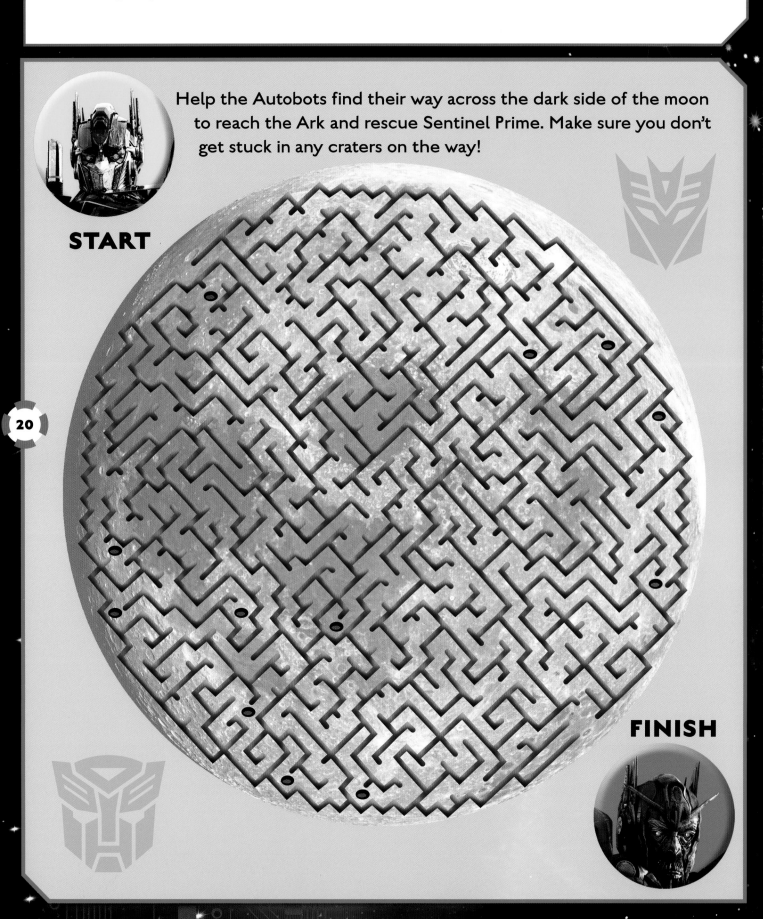

OPTIMUS PRIME

MEGATRON

PATCHWORK PARTS

Can you work out which Autobot and Decepticon spare parts have been put together to make this mechanical monster?

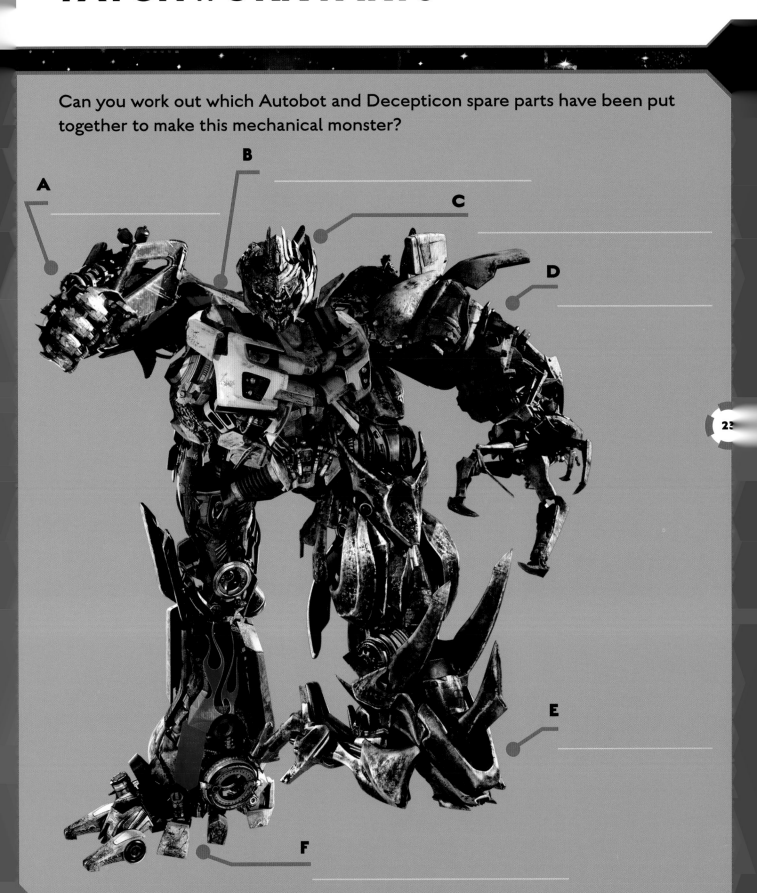

A

B

C

D

E

F

COLOUR OPTIMUS PRIME

Fearless leader of the Autobots, Optimus Prime is a formidable sight.

ROBO REPAIR

Megatron needs to repair his battle damage and reactivate himself. Find the correct circuit that leads from the neural net in his head to the power core in his chest.

The correct circuit is

DOUBLE-CROSSED!

CONTINUED FROM PAGE 19.

NEST HQ

The NEST base had never been so busy. Since the Cybertronian power source was discovered at Chernobyl, and Optimus had rescued Sentinel Prime and used the Matrix to bring him out of stasis, everything seemed to be happening at once.

The base was on high alert as Major Lennox deployed forces to battle the Decepticon attack on Washington. If that wasn't enough, Sam had just informed Lennox that the Decepticons were hunting Sentinel Prime.

The Decepticons needed Sentinel Prime to activate the mysterious Space Bridge pillars found in the wreck of the Ark. No one was sure what they were for, but you could be certain that the Decepticons wouldn't be using them for good.

"Incoming!" cried the guard at the gates of NEST HQ, pointing off along the road.

In the distance, a battle was raging. Missiles exploded and ion cannons blazed as Bumblebee, Mirage and Sideswipe clashed with three deadly Decepticons - Crankcase, Hatchet and Crowbar. Suddenly, a fire truck raced away from the battle and headed straight for the base.

"It's Sentinel Prime – open the perimeter!" ordered Major Lennox.

Ironhide and Ratchet raced to the gates just as Sentinel Prime screeched to a halt inside the compound. Looking back along the road, it seemed that the three Autobots had proved more than a match for the Decepticon attackers, and they soon joined the others inside the base.

Sam breathed a sigh of relief as he stepped out of Bumblebee and watched his friend change into robot form. Surely they must be safe inside the base?

But things weren't that simple. Sam watched in horror as Sentinel Prime raised his plasma cannon and pointed it at Ironhide. Before anyone could react, Sentinel fired a crackling pulse of plasma which ripped through Ironhide, tossing him aside in a smoking crash of twisted metal.

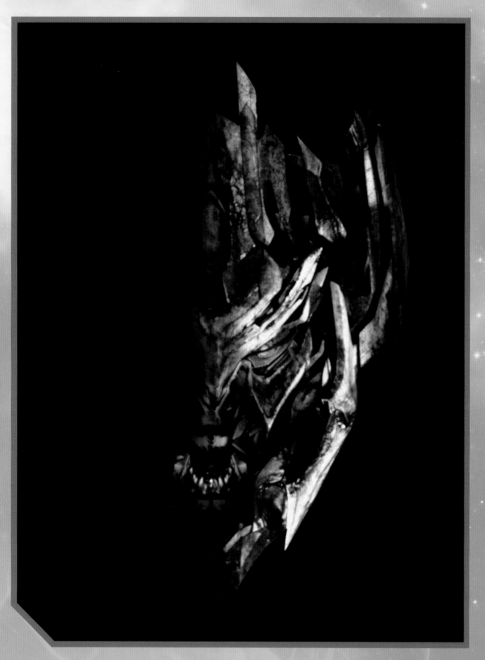

off their attack and smashed into the vault storing the five Space Bridge pillars. Stealing them, he changed into his vehicle form and raced away from the base in a cloud of dust...

The National Mall, Washington D.C.

Sentinel Prime and Megatron worked together quickly to set the five pillars at different points around the Mall.

When they were set, Sentinel powered up the Anchor Pillar and five blinding white beams of energy shot into the sky. The beams met over his head and formed a blazing dome of light.

"I am sorry, my Autobot brothers," said Sentinel, levelling his plasma cannon again. "For the sake of our planet's survival, a deal with Megatron had to be made."

No one could believe it – Sentinel Prime was a traitor!

The NEST forces opened fire, but Sentinel was too powerful. He shrugged

At the same moment, thousands of miles away on the surface of the moon, something strange was happening. In the area surrounding the crashed Ark, the ground began to tremble and shake. Dust clouds rose and the surface cracked as shadowy forms started to emerge from their hiding places.

Soon hundreds of Decepticon warriors had materialised, scattered across the grey plains as far as the eye could see. It was a hidden army, and each warrior was holding a Space Bridge pillar. Silently, the pillars began to glow until they seemed to explode in a burst of pure energy.

When the flash stopped, nothing remained on the moon. All the Decepticons had vanished, as if they were never there.

But the deadly warriors were not far away. Sentinel Prime had used the Space Bridge to transport them to Earth. The Decepticon invasion had begun...

CONTINUED ON PAGE 38.

COLOUR BUMBLEBEE

Always ready to roll out into action, Bumblebee is Sam's friend and protector.

DO NOT DISTURB!

Need some peace and quiet? Cut out this awesome door hanger and let the power of the Autobots and Decepticons keep your bedroom strictly off limits.

DO NOT DISTURB!

DANGER: RESTRICTED ZONE

UNAUTHORISED PERSONNEL WILL BE VAPORISED!

MATRIX MASTER

Spot the odd switch out in each row to help Optimus power up the Matrix and restore Sentinel Prime.

POWER PYRAMID

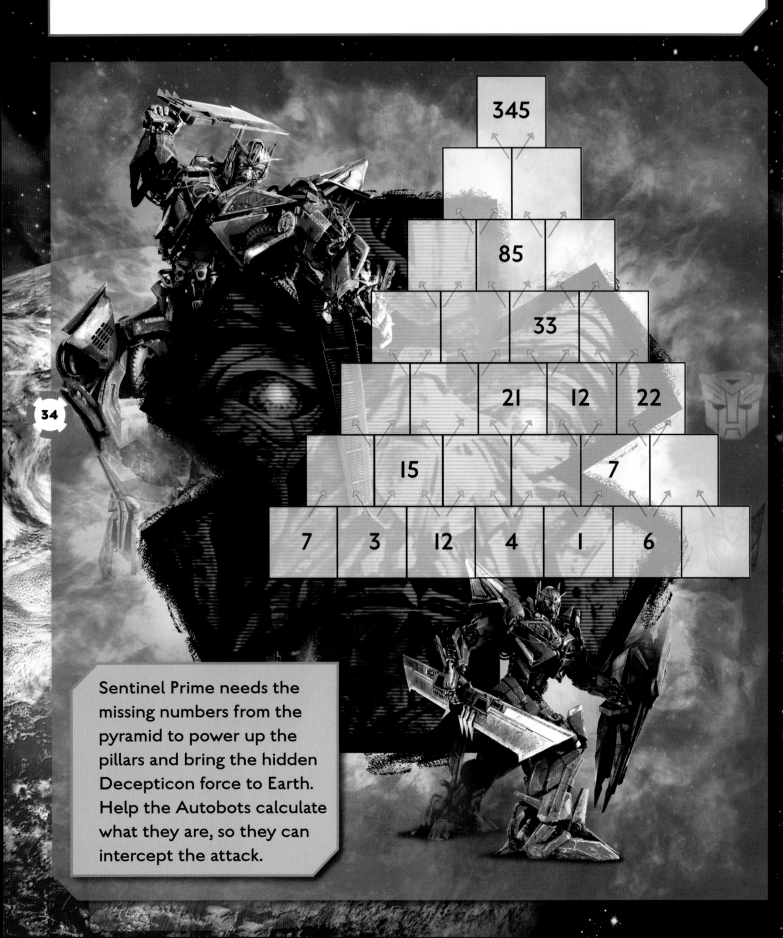

			345			
		85				
			33			
		21	12	22		
	15			7		
7	3	12	4	1	6	

Sentinel Prime needs the missing numbers from the pyramid to power up the pillars and bring the hidden Decepticon force to Earth. Help the Autobots calculate what they are, so they can intercept the attack.

COLOUR SHOCKWAVE

Shockwave is one of the latest Decepticons to threaten Earth. He is a ruthless and deadly opponent.

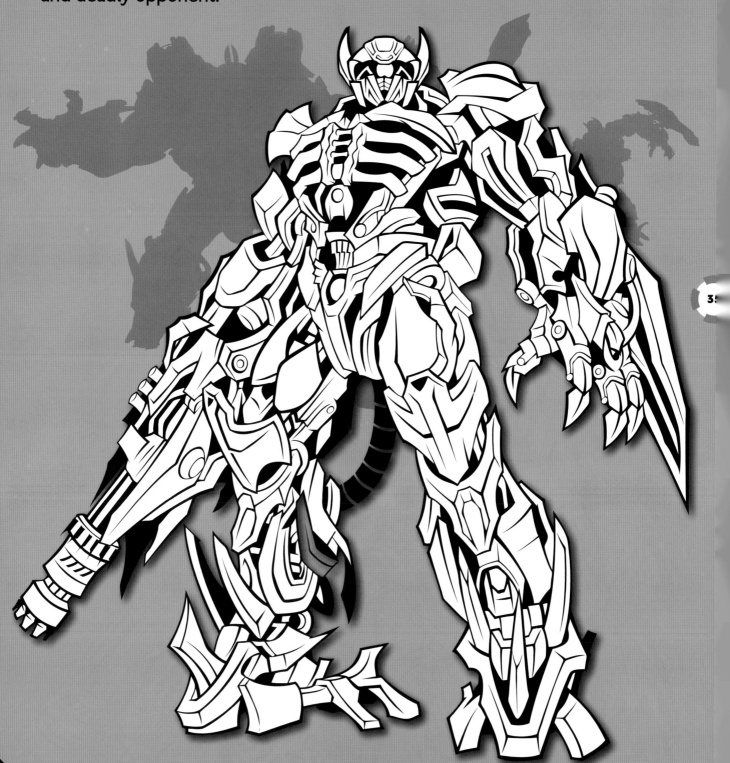

DECEPTICON DEPLOYMENT

CHICAGO, ILLINOIS, USA:
Population 2.8 million.
Highest Energon reading
detected here. Major airspace
hub, but strategic resources
minimal. High number of
tall buildings makes for ideal
interstellar transmission site.

NEW YORK, NEW YORK, USA:
Population 8.3 million.
Low resource importance.
Importance to Decepticon
deployment unknown.

MATO GROSSO, BRAZIL:
Site of recent discovery of
large amounts of iron ore.
Strategic importance of these
resources is huge.

NEST Satellite ORION: Latest Energon Emission Imaging – Space Bridge Pillar Deployment

BEIJING, CHINA:
Population 14.9 million. One of the most populated places on the planet. Energon readings also appearing in other large cities. Reason unknown.

CHERNOBYL, PRIPYAT, UKRAINE:
Highly irradiated area and site of discovery of Cybertronian Fuel Cell. Obviously a significant area for the Decepticons.

MAJNOON, IRAQ:
Decepticons detected in region of this major oil field. Protection of Earth's fossil fuels is critical.

OLYMPIC DAM, SOUTH AUSTRALIA:
Major uranium mine. Uranium is a key component in nuclear weapons. This site is designated ALPHA 1 importance.

ABANDONED!

CONTINUED FROM PAGE 29.

It was a sad day for mankind, and an especially sad day for Sam.

Battles raged all over the world – from as far away as Australia and China there were Energon readings that showed massive numbers of Decepticons descending on cities.

The terrifying attack was laying waste to whole cities, but no one had any idea that Sentinel Prime's ultimate plan would bring about something much worse.

One thing was clear to the people of Earth, though: since Optimus and the other Autobots had supported Sentinel Prime, they must be held responsible for the Decepticon invasion.

So the US government voted to banish the Autobots from Earth. Even though the planet was in grave danger, no one trusted the Autobots any more and they were being forced to leave the planet immediately...

Sam watched as the Autobot engineers worked hard at the launch site, swarming over the old, creaky body of the Autobot spacecraft, the Xantium. They crashed and bashed, tightening rivets and welding seams to get the ship ready to blast off and carry the Autobots far away from Earth.

Sam couldn't believe what he was seeing. Despite everything the Autobots had done to protect Earth, all the battles they had fought and the times they had defeated Megatron, it seemed humans could not forgive them this one mistake. It just wasn't fair.

38

As the Autobots started to board the ship, Optimus stopped and turned to Sam.

"You are my friend, Sam," he said. "You always will be. But your leaders have spoken. From here the fight will be your own." Then without waiting for a reply, he turned and disappeared inside the ship.

Sam couldn't bear it. All his friends were leaving.

With a deafening roar, the booster rockets ignited and a pillow of fire appeared under the ship. The ground shook as the Xantium slowly moved away from the launch pad, speeding faster and faster into the sky on a column of flames.

Sam peered upwards as the Xantium shrank into the heavens on its way into outer space. After a few moments there was a flash as the enormous booster rocket fell away. It drifted back to the ground on two parachutes, its job complete.

But just then, something shot across the sky, heading straight towards the Xantium. From the ground it looked like an ordinary F-22 Raptor jet fighter, but Sam knew better – it was the fearsome Decepticon warrior, Starscream.

As Sam watched in horror, Starscream

shot across the sky, gaining on the Xantium with every second. Before Sam could warn anyone, Starscream had closed in and begun to attack.

Swooping in, Starscream's cannons sprang to life, spitting fire at their target. The old Autobot spacecraft didn't stand a chance – with no way to dodge, no defence systems and no weapons, it was a sitting duck.

The attack was over in an instant.

Starscream's cannons fired with deadly accuracy, and the Xantium erupted in flames. Explosions tore through the ship, ripping it to pieces and scattering the wreckage across the sky in a cloud of expanding dust.

Sam was stunned. This couldn't be happening. Optimus, Bumblebee and the Autobots had been destroyed!

CONTINUED ON PAGE 48.

MORE THAN MEETS THE EYE

Decepticons use every weapon at their disposal to achieve their ends. Trickery is a powerful tool, and the Autobots must be on the lookout for Decepticon deceit – just take a look at the training exercises below to learn how things are not always as they seem.

ILLUSION 1

Even the simplest things are not always straightforward. Which line is longer, A or B?

ILLUSION 2

Distracting your enemy will keep it occupied while you complete your plan. Look at this triangle. Can you tell where it ends? Where does it begin?

ILLUSION 3

If your enemy does not recognise its true target, it cannot possibly win. Concentrate on these images. Which one has a bigger circle in the middle?

A

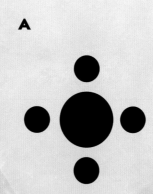

B

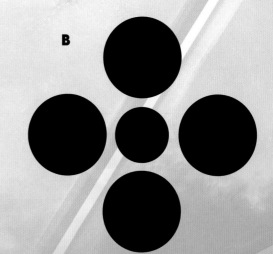

ILLUSION 4

Illusion is a powerful tool. Are there really three points on this fork? Take a closer look...

ILLUSION 5

The ultimate weapon is one that confuses your enemy and throws them off balance.

Stare closely at the cross in the middle of this image. Now slowly move the page towards and away from your face. Are the circles really moving?

CODE BREAKER

Optimus has sent Bumblebee an urgent message, but it is written in the code of the Primes! Get cracking and see if you can help Bumblebee work out what the message says before it's too late...

SHOCKWAVE

SENTINEL PRIME

DOUBLE DIFFERENCE

Can you spot six differences between these two pictures of the deadly Decepticon, Megatron?

47

SHOCK AND AWE!

CONTINUED FROM PAGE 41.

CHICAGO, U.S.A.

But the Autobots were not dead – they had escaped the craft in the first booster rocket to separate. They caught up with Sam, who had travelled to Chicago with the military from the rocket launch site. Sam couldn't believe it. He told Optimus where to find the Decepticons.

Optimus Prime streaked over the city in his flight harness, looking down on the wrecked streets and buildings below. The Autobots had tracked Sentinel Prime to Chicago. Now it was a race against time to stop him before he could use the Space Bridge to pull Cybertron to Earth and take the whole planet prisoner!

As he swooped around a skyscraper, Optimus caught sight of Shockwave and his pet Driller. Without a second thought, the fearless Autobot leader dived in to attack.

Optimus fired his ion cannons at the huge Driller without mercy. Great blasts of energy ripped into the sides of the Decepticon, tearing sparking holes in its side. Inside each hole, machinery fizzed and burned, before exploding and causing even more damage.

While the Driller was recovering, Optimus turned his fire on its wriggling tentacles. With amazing accuracy, he fired at their base and managed to blast several of them clean off. Nothing could withstand that amount of damage and survive, and it wasn't long before the Driller fell to the road with a deafening crash, left lying in a smoking, shuddering heap.

But the battle wasn't over yet. Shockwave appeared out of the wreckage and aimed his huge neutron cannon at Optimus. Almost faster than the eye could see, he opened fire again and again until the air was full of deadly plasma bolts.

Even the great Optimus Prime couldn't hope to dodge so many blasts, and one of them struck his flight harness. Trailing smoke and flames, Optimus started to spin away. Unable to control his flight, he crashed headlong into the side of a huge building. He was completely stuck.

With Optimus temporarily out of action, Shockwave turned his cannons on the other Autobots. Nearby, Bumblebee was locked in battle with Soundwave. The brave Autobot was so busy fighting that he didn't notice Shockwave appear behind him, raising his cannon to attack. There was no way that Bumblebee would be able to dodge an attack that he couldn't see coming...

But just as Shockwave was about to blast Bumblebee to shreds, something slammed into him, smashing him clean off his feet. It was Optimus! He had managed to free himself from the wrecked building and was back in action.

Without stopping for an instant, Optimus continued his attack. The two enemies were too close together to use their cannons, so this would be a hand-to-hand battle to the death...

The two mighty warriors smashed each other with their fists, sending up showers of sparks. Shockwave bucked and rolled, but he just couldn't seem to escape the grip of the heroic Autobot.

Rolling across the road, Optimus clutched Shockwave in one mighty hand while battering him with the other.

Optimus delivered blow after blow, bending metal plates and crushing vital machinery inside. Wires and motors fizzed and popped as Optimus Prime pressed home his advantage, using each attack to put his deadly enemy out of action.

With a final, crushing blow, Optimus sent Shockwave spinning to the side of the street. Tumbling end over end, the evil robot finally landed against the wall, nothing more than a twisted wreck.

Raising his eyes to the top of the building beside him, Optimus gathered his strength. There was one last enemy standing between the Autobots and victory – the traitor, Sentinel Prime. But time was running out...

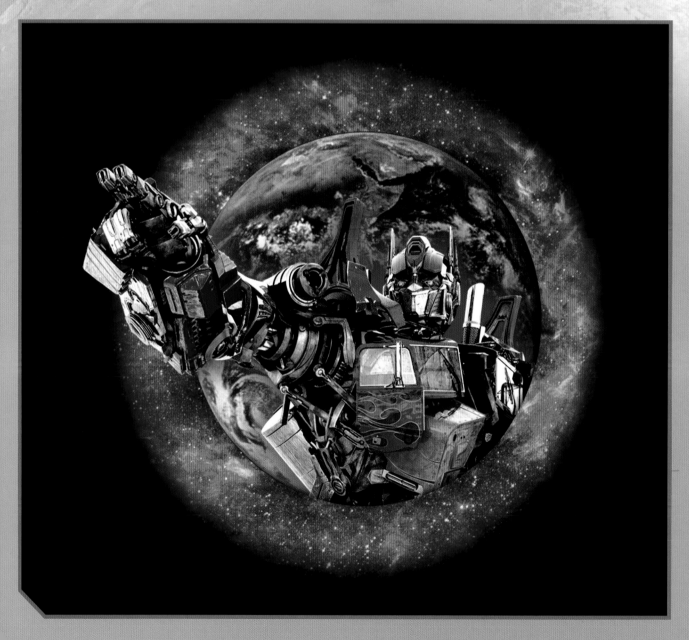

Optimus made his way to the building where Sentinel was connecting the pillars. He raised his cannon and fired at the anchor pillar, blowing the spire on which it rested to smithereens. The anchor pillar fell to the street, and Sentinel jumped down after it. The pillar was not broken – it continued to power the energy grid as it lay on the ground.

Sam, who was watching from nearby, tried to run for the pillar, but one of the Decepticons' human allies had beaten him to it. The man smiled as he pushed the symbol etched into the pillar, and a sonic boom washed over the city. The energy grid lit up in the sky, then went black. At that moment, the curvature of an enormous metal planet appeared in the sky. The man stared up at Cybertron in delighted awe, and Sam quickly knocked the pillar out of his hands while he was distracted, but it was too late. Cybertron had come to Earth.

Sam's girlfriend, Carly, had been watching Sam and the Autobots struggle, and she decided it was time to get involved. There must be something she could do to help. She ran through the streets until she found Megatron, sitting in an alley. She shouted up to him, "Your Decepticons finally conquer this planet, and yet their leader won't be you! Any minute now you'll be nothing but Sentinel's servant."

Her words worked like a charm. Megatron was furious – he knew Carly was right. Megatron ran through the streets until he reached the two Primes. He found Sentinel standing over Optimus, pointing a cosmic rust blaster straight at Optimus's chest. Megatron knocked the blaster out of Sentinel's hand and slammed into him. Together, he and Optimus wrestled with Sentinel until Optimus managed to fire Sentinel's own cosmic rust blaster straight into the traitorous Prime's chest. The corrosive element spread over Sentinel's body, and he fell to the ground.

Meanwhile soldiers had been planting explosives over and around the anchor pillar. They detonated the explosives, and the pillar exploded in a ball of flames. Cybertron began to fade, and

then disappeared completely from Earth's atmosphere.

Optimus left Sentinel on the ground, and turned to Megatron. "You will have your truce, but be gone from this place. Leave this planet so that *its* people, at least, may have peace." Sentinel reached out to Optimus with a trembling hand. "All I ever wanted was survival. You must see why I had to betray you," he gasped.

"You betrayed yourself," said Optimus, turning away. The battle was over, and Earth was saved.

TRANSFORMERS QUIZ

So you think you know all there is to know about Transformers? Then take this quiz and see if you have made use of the information in this Annual.

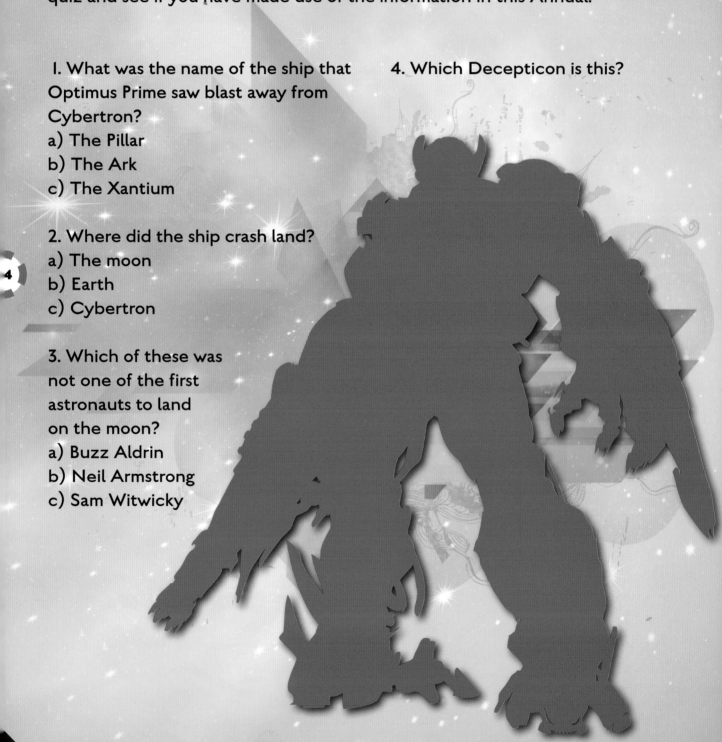

1. What was the name of the ship that Optimus Prime saw blast away from Cybertron?
a) The Pillar
b) The Ark
c) The Xantium

2. Where did the ship crash land?
a) The moon
b) Earth
c) Cybertron

3. Which of these was not one of the first astronauts to land on the moon?
a) Buzz Aldrin
b) Neil Armstrong
c) Sam Witwicky

4. Which Decepticon is this?

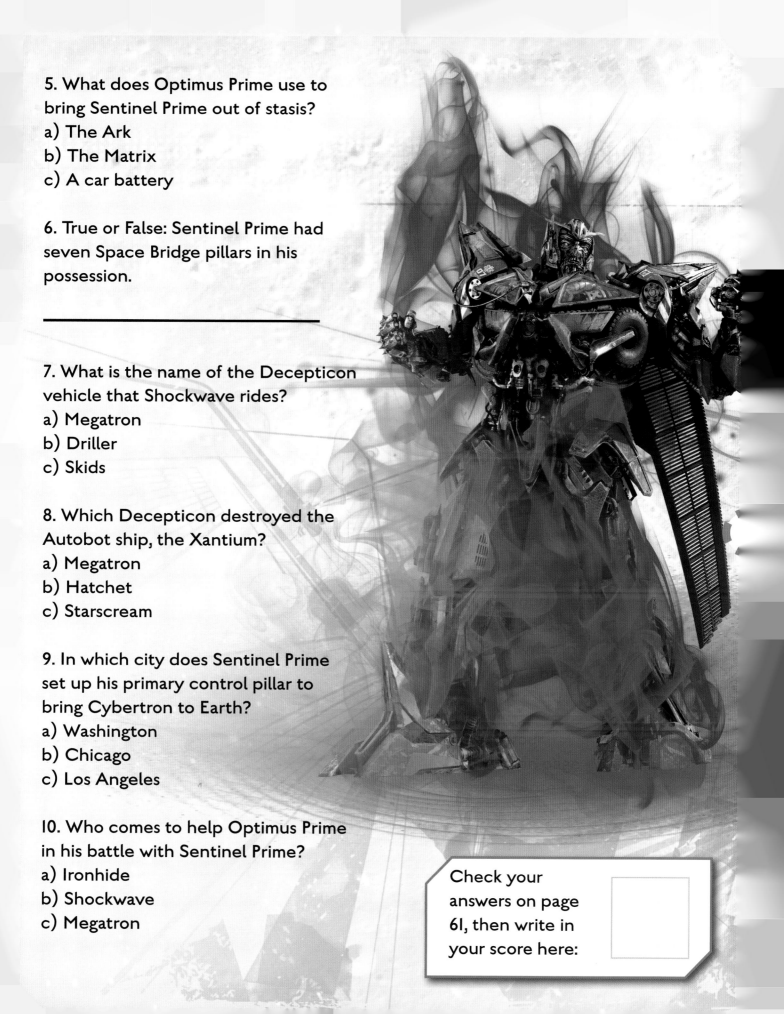

5. What does Optimus Prime use to bring Sentinel Prime out of stasis?
a) The Ark
b) The Matrix
c) A car battery

6. True or False: Sentinel Prime had seven Space Bridge pillars in his possession.

_____

7. What is the name of the Decepticon vehicle that Shockwave rides?
a) Megatron
b) Driller
c) Skids

8. Which Decepticon destroyed the Autobot ship, the Xantium?
a) Megatron
b) Hatchet
c) Starscream

9. In which city does Sentinel Prime set up his primary control pillar to bring Cybertron to Earth?
a) Washington
b) Chicago
c) Los Angeles

10. Who comes to help Optimus Prime in his battle with Sentinel Prime?
a) Ironhide
b) Shockwave
c) Megatron

Check your answers on page 61, then write in your score here:

COLOUR MEGATRON

Optimus Prime's greatest enemy, Megatron, is a tough and resourceful foe.

NEST FIELD GUIDE TO AUTOBOTS AND DECEPTICONS

CONFIDENTIAL DATA

KEY: 1 = HIGHEST THREAT/STRENGTH LEVEL
5 = LOWEST THREAT/STRENGTH LEVEL

NAME: Megatron
AFFILIATION: Decepticon
WEAPONS: Ion-fused chain whip.
Plasma cannon
DISGUISE: Cybertronian tank or jet
THREAT LEVEL: DEFCON 1

LATEST INTEL: After his aborted
attempt to revive The Fallen and
destroy the planet, Megatron
fled into the desert. Still our
deadliest threat, his current
whereabouts are unknown. However
NEST believes Megatron is merely
biding his time before his next
attack. DESTROY ON SIGHT.

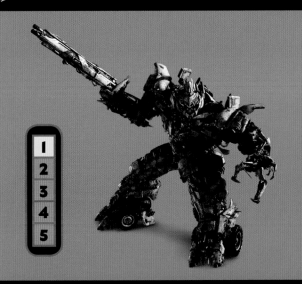

NAME: Bumblebee
AFFILIATION: Autobot/Sam Witwicky
WEAPONS: Dual plasma cannons
DISGUISE: Chevrolet Camaro sports car
STRENGTH LEVEL: OMEGA 2

LATEST INTEL: Although still a brave and loyal Autobot ally, Bumblebee's devotion to civilian Sam Witwicky means that he may prove unpredictable. However, his commitment to defending the planet against the Decepticons cannot be questioned.

1
2
3
4
5

NAME: Shockwave
AFFILIATION: Decepticon
WEAPONS: Multi-pulse neutron cannon
DISGUISE: None — rides in cockpit of Cybertronian Driller
THREAT LEVEL: DEFCON 1

LATEST INTEL: Little is known about this latest deadly foe. According to Optimus Prime, Shockwave is a calculating, ruthless enemy. Shockwave seems to have control of a Cybertronian Driller, and uses it to help him move around. Second only to Megatron in terms of threat level, we believe after the events at Chernobyl it is better to contain this enemy before it is too late. DESTROY ON SIGHT.

1
2
3
4
5

NAME: Skids & Mudflap
AFFILIATION: Autobot
WEAPONS: Ion cannons
DISGUISE: Concept cars
STRENGTH LEVEL: OMEGA 4

LATEST INTEL: Even though they argue all the time, when it comes to data retrieval and collection, these Autobot twins are second to none. Highly intelligent and with a neural link that borders on the psychic, they are also extremely brave in battle.

1
2
3
4
5

NAME: Ironhide
AFFILIATION: Autobot
WEAPONS: Ion-charged gatling, multi-function missile launchers
DISGUISE: GMC SUV truck
STRENGTH LEVEL: OMEGA 3

LATEST INTEL: Next to Optimus Prime himself, Ironhide is one of our most powerful allies. Tough and efficient, Ironhide is the Autobot's weapons expert and packs a serious punch. If you're stuck in a hole, Ironhide has the firepower and tactical expertise to dig you out of it.

1
2
3
4
5

NAME: Optimus Prime
AFFILIATION: Autobot
WEAPONS: Ion blaster, plasma sword
DISGUISE: Huge articulated truck cab
STRENGTH LEVEL: OMEGA 1

LATEST INTEL: Despite apparently being destroyed in the last battle with Megatron, Optimus was restored by the Matrix and is now in full operation once more. Central to our plans to defeat the Decepticons, Optimus Prime is a fearless ally who will stop at nothing to protect our world.

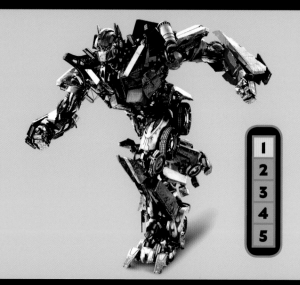

1
2
3
4
5

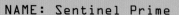

NAME: Sentinel Prime
AFFILIATION: Decepticon — Autobot traitor
WEAPONS: Plasma cannon
DISGUISE: Fire truck
STRENGTH LEVEL: DEFCON 1

LATEST INTEL: Kept in stasis in a crashed spaceship on the moon, Sentinel Prime was revived by our ally Optimus Prime. Originally the leader of the Autobots and keeper of five pillars of the Space Bridge, Sentinel Prime is actually a traitor and has struck a deal with the Decepticons. DESTROY ON SIGHT.

1
2
3
4
5

ANSWERS

12 DATA DELIVERY

Z	S	U	S	O	P	T	I	M	U	S	P	R	I	M	E	Y	I	K	U
S	J	K	Q	H	L	M	T	V	E	L	W	P	D	X	H	P	H	N	G
C	W	U	I	X	M	U	D	F	L	A	P	P	C	O	W	O	B	P	J
Y	L	Z	F	D	P	D	V	E	L	N	L	N	F	N	P	D	J	J	Z
O	O	A	Q	M	S	S	B	A	G	C	Q	Q	B	B	W	P	R	Z	E
L	V	R	K	U	Q	Y	A	U	N	D	D	X	D	S	M	T	E	V	Q
M	F	K	E	M	I	R	P	L	E	N	I	T	N	E	S	T	A	I	G
J	J	I	F	Z	D	F	K	U	Q	F	B	O	Z	V	C	W	J	Z	Z
M	R	L	F	W	B	S	C	S	L	K	Y	M	M	G	K	A	N	T	G
G	N	A	W	J	C	M	K	O	Y	N	X	X	M	C	K	P	A	Y	P
L	Z	I	N	S	T	E	Y	R	O	S	X	P	O	M	D	V	S	Q	N
E	R	Z	H	C	O	G	F	P	M	D	C	H	W	S	R	M	D	B	O
E	R	U	N	P	L	A	C	I	J	R	S	V	M	M	L	R	D	L	R
D	F	A	E	V	M	T	H	X	J	A	Y	W	D	A	Q	V	U	E	T
I	F	G	T	O	X	R	O	B	K	A	T	N	M	S	T	M	W	P	R
H	E	N	J	E	L	O	F	M	L	V	D	G	T	P	L	H	J	A	E
N	Y	C	P	Y	V	N	R	K	N	X	X	K	M	M	W	P	Z	G	B
O	L	L	C	X	H	G	D	H	V	P	O	E	Q	T	O	C	S	J	Y
R	N	S	I	D	E	S	W	I	P	E	W	M	U	I	Y	O	W	F	C
I	D	J	M	Y	Y	B	D	O	V	G	G	F	H	U	S	U	N	V	C

13 BITS AND BYTES

1 = F
2 = H
3 = A
4 = E
5 = D

23 PATCHWORK PARTS

A = SENTINEL
B = BUMBLEBEE
C = MEGATRON
D = MEGATRON
E = SHOCKWAVE
F = OPTIMUS

20 MOON MAZE

25 ROBO REPAIR

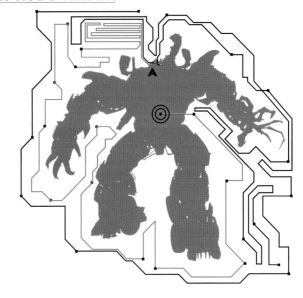

33 MATRIX MASTER

A = 4
B = 5
C = 1
D = 3
E = 2

34 POWER PYRAMID

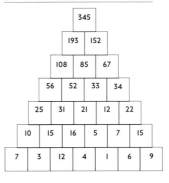

		345			
	193		152		
108		85		67	
56	52		33	34	
25	31	21	12	22	
10	15	16	5	7	15
7	3	12	4	1	6	9

47 DOUBLE DIFFERENCE

42 MORE THAN MEETS THE EYE

Illusion I: Both A and B are the same length
Illusion 3: Both A and B are the same size

44 CODE BREAKER

SENTINEL PRIME IS A TRAITOR. PILLAR LOCATED IN CHICAGO.

54 TRANSFORMERS QUIZ

1. The Ark
2. The moon
3. Sam Witwicky
4. Shockwave
5. The Matrix
6. False - he has five
7. Driller
8. Starscream
9. Chicago
10. Megatron